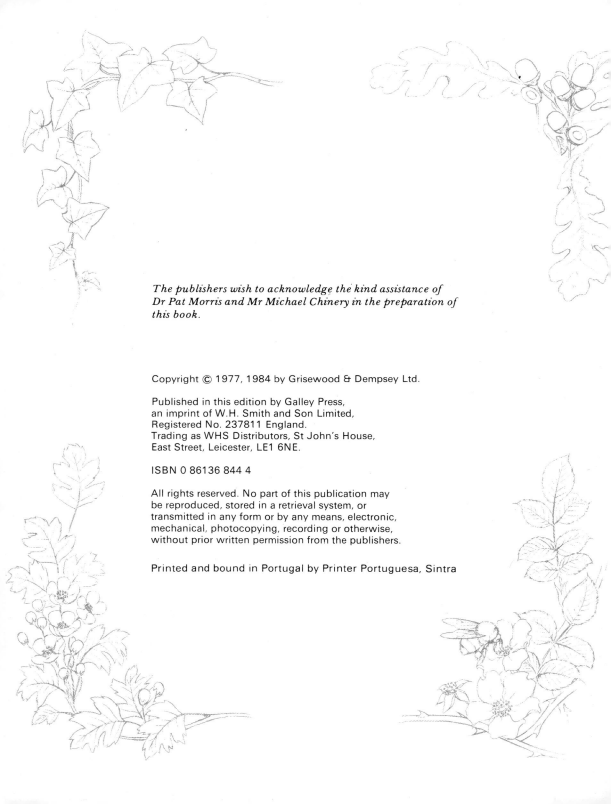

The publishers wish to acknowledge the kind assistance of
Dr Pat Morris and Mr Michael Chinery in the preparation of
this book.

Copyright © 1977, 1984 by Grisewood & Dempsey Ltd.

Published in this edition by Galley Press,
an imprint of W.H. Smith and Son Limited,
Registered No. 237811 England.
Trading as WHS Distributors, St John's House,
East Street, Leicester, LE1 6NE.

ISBN 0 86136 844 4

Printed and bound in Portugal by Printer Portuguesa, Sintra

The Mouse

By Angela Sheehan
Illustrated by Maurice Pledger

Galley Press

It was a warm, windy night. Clouds covered the moon and stars, and hid their light. In the blackness, even an owl's sharp eyes could not see the mouse as she scratched among the leaves. And the sound of her scampering feet could not be heard above the noise of rustling leaves. The mouse was safe.

She ate her fill of grass shoots and insects. Then she started back along the path to the nest where her five babies were sleeping. As she ran along the track, the clouds began to drift away from the moon. Its bright light struck the mouse's sleek fur and suddenly she was in danger. A weasel had caught a brief glimpse of her. Now, rooted to the spot, she hid behind a clump of grass, watching the gleam in the weasel's eyes as it sought her out again.

The wind blew. The grass wavered. And the light shone. The mouse stroked her whiskers in terror. But the weasel could no longer see her. After a while it caught the scent of a vole and dashed away to catch it. Safe again, the mouse hurried back to her home under the oak tree.

Deep inside the burrow, the babies were safe and warm. They had never seen the world outside and did not know of all the dangers in the woods. They slept for most of the time and sucked milk from their mother. But it would not be long before they had to learn how to find food for themselves and escape the many enemies that waited for them in the darkness.

As soon as the young mice could move about, they explored the long tunnels in their burrow. Sometimes they peeped out of the entrance holes to see what the world was like. But it was quite some time before they dared to go out.

The first time they went out, they followed
their mother a little way. But then an owl hooted
from a nearby tree and the whole family fled back
to the nest.

The young mice did not feel safe in the woods.
The chill wind ruffled their fur. And the strange
new smells and noises frightened them. Even close
by their burrow they could smell all kinds of plants
and other animals, especially other mice. And there
was so much noise that the young mice had to
listen really hard to catch the squeaks of their
nest mates.

After a few days, the young mice grew less afraid. But they were still careful when they went out alone. They knew the woods were full of watching eyes and listening ears. All kinds of animals were ready to pounce on them at their first careless squeak or movement. So the mice learned to run quickly and quietly, and to hide when the moon shone too brightly.

The young mice soon left their mother's nest for good and dug new burrows for themselves. At night they found tasty buds and grubs to eat.

But they were not all lucky enough to escape
their enemies. One was killed by a weasel that had
sneaked into his burrow. Two more were caught
on different nights by a tawny owl that swooped
silently down from its perch in a beech tree.
Another was almost killed by a prowling fox cub.

The mother mouse did not know what was
happening to her young. After they left her, she
stayed in the nest each day as usual, and went out
to find food at night. One night she went farther
into the wood than usual. She was just scratching
about by a hawthorn tree when she heard the
sound of another mouse.

The mouse was a large male that lived by the
roots of the hawthorn. The two animals sniffed at
each other until they felt that they knew each other
well. Then the male mouse climbed on to the
female's back and they mated. It was too
dangerous for them to stay together for long, where
a hungry animal might find them. So afterwards
they both ran back to the safety of their burrows.

Just three weeks and three days after she had
mated, the mother mouse gave birth to a new litter.
It was the third family she had had that summer.
The six babies were small and pink. When they were
born they could not see or hear. All they could do
was suck milk and squeak. But soon their fur grew
thick and sleek and their eyes grew big and black.

Their mother often left them curled up asleep
together while she went out to eat the seeds and
insects that were thick upon the woodland floor.
One night she stayed out for so long that the
sun was already glimmering through the trees when
she set off for home.

Knowing that her hungry babies were waiting
for her, the mouse ran as quickly as she could.
But as she approached the nest she stopped short
and stared. A dreadful sight met her eyes. Her
carefully hidden burrow was in ruins. The entrance
was broken down. Stones and soil littered the
ground. And the grass that had lined the nursery
was scattered all around. A badger's footprints led
away from the burrow.

The mouse turned away. She knew that all her babies were dead. And she knew that she would be dead, too, if she did not quickly find a place to hide. The birds were already singing in the trees above. Insects were buzzing among the dew-laden flowers. And the creatures that slept by night were waking up to a new day. The woods seemed very big and busy. But the mouse was all alone.

Quietly she sniffed around for a hiding place, and found a rotting log by the side of the stream. Its wood had crumbled into holes. She tested one with her whiskers to see if she would fit inside it. Then she squeezed her way into the hole, curled her tail round her body, and went slowly to sleep.

When she woke up again, it was night. She
slipped out of the log, looked about, and listened
for enemies. All was silent and safe. Not daring to
move far from her safe hideout, she quickly made a
tiny hole in the bank beneath the log. She dug out
the soil with her paws and squeezed her way into
the earth.

Soon she had made a tunnel about three times
as long as her body. At the end she scooped out a
hole. Then she ran back to the entrance, cleared
the soil away, and dragged some grass into the hole
to make a soft lining.

Digging tunnels was hard work for the mouse. After she had made the first one, she rested. Then she set about making another. All night she worked until she had made four strong tunnels. Now she had a fine home where she could bring up a new family. But first she must find a new mate.

Safe inside the burrow she went to sleep for the day. When she woke, it was dark and she was hungry. She knew that the woods were full of food: branches weighed down with berries; grasses heavy with seeds; thick juicy roots and fat toadstools; slugs and snails; and tasty insects. She ate her fill of them and carried some back to the nest as a store. A few days later she hid a pile of berries in a hole near her burrow. Every night she ate and collected more and more.

One night she went to the hazel tree. Like all the mice that lived nearby, she loved to eat hazel nuts. Gnawing a hole in the shell took a long time and made a lot of noise. But the mouse was enjoying herself so much that she did not notice the noise. Nor did she notice that another mouse was listening to her. It was the same mouse that she had met by the hawthorn. He, too, had come to collect hazel nuts, but was quick to hide when he heard another animal approaching.

He hid behind the tree and peeped out to see what the noise was. When he saw the mouse, he scampered over to her and they mated again.

Just over three weeks later, the mouse gave birth to yet another litter. The weather was growing colder and windier now, and the days were growing shorter. The mouse spent a lot of time in the nest. She had plenty of nuts and berries to eat. Her babies grew quickly. Soon they, too, were able to eat the softer berries and wash their fur and whiskers. They dashed up and down the tunnels, popping their heads out of holes or playing together on the bank outside the nest at night. Their mother kept a close watch on them all the time.

One night a terrible rumbling sound shook the whole wood. Bright lights flashed across the sky and lit up the trees. Rain poured down. All through the woods the animals were afraid. A great clap of thunder frightened a herd of deer so much that they ran blindly in all directions.

One young deer made for the bank where the mice lived. His hoof hit the log above the burrow and it slipped down the bank, carrying part of the bank, the nest, and all the young mice with it.

The mice were soaking wet and squeaking
with fear as the water in the ditch swirled round
them. Too young to be able to swim, they clung
helplessly to slippery clumps of grass, while their
mother tried to save them. As soon as she had
scrambled on to the bank, she reached out to drag
them from the water. Two of the mice were too far
away for her to reach. And as she pulled the others
from the flood, these two were swept away by it.

Leaving the three wet mice on the bank, she
scampered off to find a hole that was sheltered
from the rain. She found one in a tree stump and
then went back to the ditch to fetch her shivering
babies. They were too big to carry, so she led them,
slipping and sliding, to safety.

By morning the storm was over, but the woods were still wet and muddy. Broken branches and leaves lay everywhere. The mouse picked her way through them back to the bank where her burrow had been. Luckily, only part of the burrow had been destroyed. So she set to work to repair it, digging deeper into the bank and collecting new grass.

When she had finished, she went to the tree stump and led her weary babies back to the nest. But still she could not rest. All the nuts and berries in her food store had been scattered. She must find them all and bring them back. Even though it was daylight, she bravely ran backwards and forwards picking up the nuts and berries until she was so tired that she could work no longer.

The nest in the bank was now as good as new, but the young mice would not be there for long. They soon stopped drinking their mother's milk and at night they went out on their own. They were old enough now to look after themselves.

When they finally left their mother's nest, the weather was much colder. So first they had to dig new burrows to protect themselves from the wind and rain, as well as from their enemies. Most of them tunnelled into the ground near their mother's nest. But one mouse found an empty thrush's nest in a holly bush. It was big enough for her and for a small store of berries. She would be quite safe there for the winter. And in spring she would be able to rear a family there.

During the winter it was so cold that the mother mouse sometimes stayed in her burrow for days and nights on end. Even when snow covered the ground above, the burrow was warm, and she could sleep or run about in the tunnels quite safely. She did not need much food because she had eaten so much in the autumn.

One day she was woken from her sleep by a scratching noise coming from her food store. She ran down the tunnel, only to discover that a squirrel was stealing her nuts. The squirrels never remembered where they buried their own nuts. So they just took any they found.

The mouse waited until the squirrel had eaten its fill and gone back to its tree. Then she moved the few nuts that were left to a deeper part of the burrow and closed up the hole above. She did not really need the nuts. Now that her family had gone, she had little to do but search for food.

But as the winter wore on, there was less and less food in the woods. And there seemed to be more animals looking for it. Even the yellow-necked mice were coming into the woods now that food was scarce in the hedgerows and cornfields. All the animals were hungry, except those lucky ones that slept soundly beneath the ground.

The woodland stayed cold for months. Then
new shoots sprang from the ground, delicate
flowers bloomed, and insects crawled over the forest
floor. There would be lots of food for the mouse to
eat in the warm, sunny months to come.

More About Mice

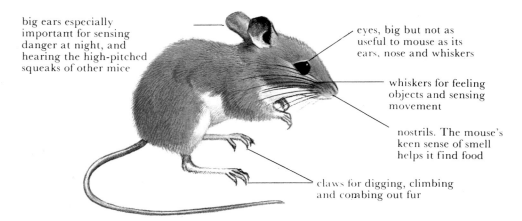

big ears especially important for sensing danger at night, and hearing the high-pitched squeaks of other mice

eyes, big but not as useful to mouse as its ears, nose and whiskers

whiskers for feeling objects and sensing movement

nostrils. The mouse's keen sense of smell helps it find food

claws for digging, climbing and combing out fur

The body of a wood mouse

Mice belong to a group of animals called rodents. Rodents are animals that gnaw. They have large chisel-shaped front teeth. These teeth are worn down all the time as the animal gnaws but they never wear out because they never stop growing.

The mouse in the story is the wood mouse, or long-tailed field mouse. It is related to other kinds of mice as well as to rats, squirrels, voles, guinea pigs and beavers. It is quite a big mouse: its body is ten centimetres long and its tail is as long again.

A Mouse's House

The wood mouse's burrow is usually a network of underground tunnels with a 'nursery' for rearing the young and 'storerooms' for food. The entrances are only about four centimetres wide. From them lead set pathways which the mice follow over and over again when they go out for food.

The wood mouse keeps its nest and its body as clean as possible. It combs its fur with its claws.

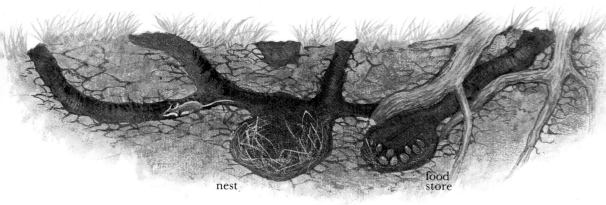

nest

food store

A wood mouse's burrow. It is about 1½ metres from side to side

More and More Mice

The wood mouse has as many as five litters each year with up to six babies in each. The babies are suckled by their mother for three weeks after they are born. They grow quickly and five months later are ready to breed themselves. They live for about two years if they are not caught by any enemies.

Enemies Everywhere

Wherever mice live they are in constant danger. People kill them because they steal food from farms and homes. And they seem to be a favourite food of meat-eating animals. Owls are their main enemies; mice sometimes make up a third of all the food they eat. Other enemies are weasels, stoats and foxes.

The wood mouse can run fast to escape its enemies and can jump more than a metre. But it is not safe even in its nest.

What Mice Eat

The wood mouse's favourite food is grain (the seeds of grasses). It also eats other seeds, young plants and buds, fruit and nuts, and mushrooms and toadstools. Sometimes wood mice eat insects and snails as well. A special treat for them is honey which they steal from bees' nests.

Whenever there is lots of food, the wood mice gather it up and store it under the ground or maybe in a hollow tree. People often think that squirrels bury hoards of nuts. But in fact they only bury nuts one at a time. The true hoarder is the wood mouse.

Yellow-necked mouse

House mouse

Harvest mouse

Dormouse

Edible dormouse

**Some other kinds of mice. They all have similar tracks.
The dormice are only distant cousins of the other three**